CW00376776

How Devon Changed the World

(a bit)

Paul White

Bossiney Books

This reprint 2020
First published 2017 by
Bossiney Books Ltd, 33 Queens Drive, Ilkley, LS29 9QW
www.bossineybooks.com

ISBN 978-1-906474-61-4

Acknowledgements
We are grateful to the Orestone Manor Hotel for kindly allowing us to use their
image of the first Christmas card on page 29.

Printed in Great Britain by R Booth Ltd, Penryn, Cornwall

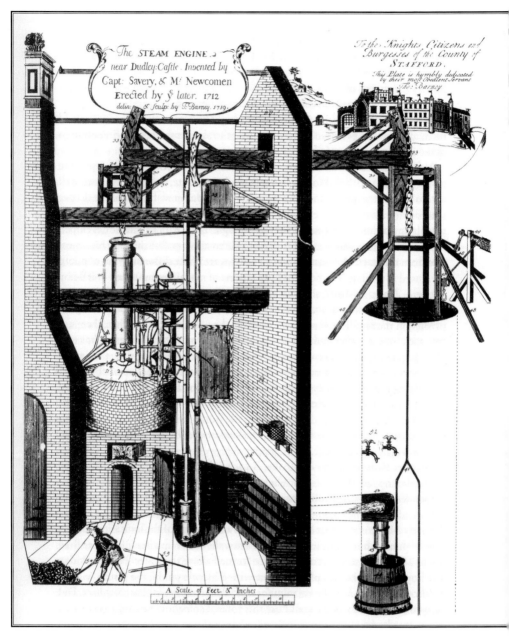

The first known Newcomen engine was erected in 1712 at the
Coneygree Coalworks, Dudley, in the West Midlands

Inventors and inventions

The steam pumping engine

This was the machine which set the Industrial Revolution in motion, by making coal and mineral mines much more productive. It marked the change from dependence on human and animal power to mechanisation. It happened 50 years before James Watt came up with his improved design, and it was the invention of two Devonians, Thomas Savery (c.1650-1715), a gentleman and military engineer, and the craftsman and businessman Thomas Newcomen (1664-1729).

Savery, who was born at Shilstone near Modbury, took out a patent in 1698 for 'raising water by the impellent force of fire' and demonstrated his model of a 'fire engine', or as we know it a steam engine, to King William III and to the Royal Society in 1699.

He erected several larger engines, but whilst the model had worked well, the design was flawed: its problems increased as the engine was scaled up – the greater the pressure that was created within the engine, the more heat was lost – and the more likely it was to explode. It also required someone (Savery said it could be a boy of 13) to open and close taps four times a minute, as well as stoking the fire – and the fire had to be underground, which would have been highly dangerous in most mines.

Although Savery made improvements, his 'fire engine' never worked well enough to drain a mine. Nevertheless his patent, which should have ended in 1713, was extended to 1733 just one year after it was first granted, by Act of Parliament – but possibly through the King's interference.

Thomas Newcomen was an 'ironmonger' at Dartmouth, whose main business was to design, manufacture and supply tools to mines in Devon and Cornwall, not just in iron, but also in copper and brass. The Devon mines could be drained using water-wheels to power bucket chains, but in West Cornwall the mines were deeper and there were few streams strong enough to power a water-wheel, so they were dependent on horsepower.

Newcomen probably knew Savery, whose work for the Commissioners for Sick and Hurt Seamen took him to Dartmouth.

When Newcomen came up with a different design for an 'atmospheric engine' which actually worked, it is generally assumed he was obliged to go into partnership with Savery. However, the background to their association is not known and there may have been advantages to both sides: indeed, perhaps it was Newcomen's firm which had constructed Savery's machines, and it is highly unlikely that a non-conformist tradesman from Dartmouth would ever have succeeded in getting a royal patent at that time.

Whereas Savery's machine was a syphon which drew water into itself, Newcomen's drove a piston in an adjacent cylinder, and the piston then worked a beam engine.

As well as being an engineer and 'ironmonger', Newcomen was a baptist minister, with numerous contacts who rapidly spread the news of his invention, particularly in London and in the Black Country. It is noticeable that many developments in trade and industry during the 18th and early 19th centuries were either created within, or spread by, this kind of non-conformist network.

The first known engine of this type was built for the Coneygree Coalworks near Dudley in 1712, but it is likely that there was an earlier engine built in Cornwall, at Wheal Vor, which had tried a Savery engine in 1698 and may have installed a Newcomen version in 1710. It was in use there until 1715 when the mine temporarily closed.

When the Savery patent expired in 1733, there were 125 Newcomen engines at work, and by 1775 no fewer than 600 had been built, changing the nature of coal extraction in particular. The Newcomen engine was very inefficient in its use of coal; after 1775 James Watt's engine, with a separate condenser and rotary motion, was a serious challenger and many users abandoned their Newcomen engines. But the Watt engine was far more complex, and Boulton & Watt demanded large royalties, so in those areas where coal was cheap the Newcomen engine remained competitive until the expiry of Boulton & Watt's patent in 1790.

We are very lucky to be able to see a Newcomen engine, one which was originally installed in 1725 at the Griff colliery near Coventry, still in operation – though not using steam – at the Dartmouth Visitor Centre.

The computer and central heating

If the invention of the steam engine was Devon's greatest single contribution to a changing world, it can also claim a role in that more recent game-changer, the computer, through the pioneering work of Charles Babbage (1791-1871).

His parents Benjamin Babbage and Betsy Plumleigh née Teape were both from wealthy Totnes families. Charles' father was a banker, his paternal grandfather having been a goldsmith and mayor of Totnes in 1754. His maternal grandfather had been mayor in 1757. Charles was almost certainly born at his parents' London home on 26 December 1791, and baptised at St Mary Newington on 6 January 1792. He was to spend much of his life in London, but part of his education was in Devon, his father retired to Devon in 1803, and Charles married Georgiana Whitmore in Teignmouth in 1814.

He went to Cambridge University in 1810, but found the maths teaching extremely dull by the standards he was used to. He left without a degree – due to his attempt to argue 'that God was a material agent' being declared blasphemous by the examiner.

As he had a small private income he had no need to earn a living, and when his father died in 1827 he inherited a fortune. He was able to travel, particularly studying methods of manufacturing both in Britain and abroad. He participated enthusiastically in London's learned societies as a scientific polymath and inventor.

He was a great socialiser, hosting Saturday soirées for the London intelligentsia, and apparently also a great raconteur.

Babbage produced the first opthalmoscope for studying the interior of the eye, but London's opticians were too short-sighted to adopt it. In 1832 his most successful work was published, *On the Economy of Machinery and Manufactures*, which was an encyclopaedic summary of mechanical techniques in use both in Britain and Europe. In it he advocated a decimal currency, as well as the use of tidal power for energy in place of coal. The book went through several editions, was translated into six languages and had an influence on both John Stuart Mill and Karl Marx.

But from 1821 a great deal of Babbage's energy went into the development of a calculating machine, known as a difference engine.

From an early age he had been fascinated by the repetitive calculations necessary to create mathematical tables – tables for trigonometry, astronomy and navigation, but also the books of logarithms which were used before pocket calculators were available and were vital for practical use by engineers, sailors and others. These tables were produced by teams of 'computers' – which at that time meant arithmetical clerks – and were liable to human error.

Babbage had been seeking since at least 1821 to design a calculating machine able to undertake this work without error. He was successful in obtaining government grants towards the construction of his calculator and by 1832 the maker of precision machinery Joseph Clement had constructed on Babbage's behalf about 15% of 'Difference Engine Number 1', consisting of 12,000 parts. Another 12,000 parts had been manufactured but not assembled. Had it ever been completed, it would have been huge, and have weighed 15 tonnes.

The government had by this stage contributed the vast sum for those days of £17,478. At this point Babbage and Clement had a major row: some sources say that Babbage insisted on moving the project to a new workshop, others that Babbage objected to some standard conditions of Clements' trade, but the upshot was that Clement refused to work on the project any longer. And that was the end of it – except that a version of the machine was built at the Science Museum in 2002.

When Babbage designed an improved version, the government understandably refused to fund it.

The break with Clement probably came about because Babbage was liable to outbursts of uncontrollable anger. The first biography of him was entitled *The Irascible Genius*: over the years he made a series of scathing attacks on the scientific establishment, the organisers of the Great Exhibition, and on various individuals, in a way that didn't help his own cause.

He also campaigned very publicly against the street musicians who made it hard for him to concentrate on his work (and that was before they acquired amplifiers!) as well as children playing tip-cat in the street or rolling hoops. These campaigns, however sensible, made him unpopular – and attracted street musicians to play under his window.

But Babbage was not deterred by the fate of his difference engines, which were mere calculators. He moved on, and came up with the idea of a programmable 'analytical machine'. This would be worked by the same kind of punch card system as the Jacquard loom. The machine was never built, but the idea was brilliantly explained in a publication of 1843 by the mathematician Lady Ada Augusta Lovelace. The most extraordinary thing about Ada Lovelace was not that she was a gifted mathematician at a time when women weren't normally given any mathematical education, but that she was the only legitimate daughter of the mercurial poet Byron, described by one of his lovers as 'mad, bad and dangerous to know' – not someone one might have expected to father 'the world's first computer programmer'.

Whereas the difference engine was a mere calculator, the analytical machine is a concept much nearer to a computer – but it was never built. Dr Doron Swade, a great expert on Babbage, has written in the *Oxford Dictionary of National Biography* that 'the direct influence of Babbage's work on the electronic computer is tenuous'.

Indeed by failing to make good use of his huge funding from the government Babbage very probably deterred them from investing in other people's projects.

On the other hand, Lady Ada's explanation of Babbage's analytical machine, with its first use of a machine algorithm, and her suggestions for a wide range of uses to which an analytical engine might be put – even including musical composition – was republished in 1953 and may have had some impact on subsequent developments. What is unclear is the relative contributions of Babbage and his 'dear and much admired interpreter' Lady Ada to that explanation.

Whereas Babbage had failed to make his calculating machine work, another contemporary Devonian – today almost totally unknown – succeeded. This was Thomas Fowler (1777-1843). A trade directory of 1839 describes him as a 'Bookseller, stationer & printer' in Great Torrington, but in 1830 he was a 'printer, stationer and organist' and in 1841 he described himself as a banker. His was the only bank in Torrington. He was also Treasurer of the Poor Law Union, which required him to make numerous calculations, probably to assess what poor rates each householder owed, and it was for this purpose that he invented his own calculating machine.

It was not his first invention. In 1828 he had patented the 'thermo-siphon' – an idea which was the principle behind all central heating systems until the combi-boiler arrived in the 1980s. The first to be installed was at Bicton Park, probably in a hothouse, because there was an enthusiastic article in the *Gardener's Magazine*:

> Mr Fowler has had the good fortune to hit on the idea that
> water may be heated and made to circulate through a siphon,
> as well as through horizontal pipes, or by force through pipes
> in any direction; provided always, that the height of the siphon
> be not greater than to be counter-balanced by the pressure of
> the atmosphere; say not greater than 30 feet. Any person might
> have discovered the same thing by reflection, or in answer to the
> question asked; but we are not aware that the idea has occurred,
> either to the original inventor of the hot-water system,
> Bonnemain; to its introducers into England, Bolton and Watt...
> or to any of the numerous engineers now occupied in applying
> this mode of heating.

Unfortunately for Fowler, his idea was promptly seized upon by many rivals, and he was quite unable to afford the expensive legal procedures which *might* have protected the rights of his patent – might, because there were and are limitations on patenting a broad idea rather than a piece of machinery. Fowler did not make his fortune from the thermosiphon, as he had hoped, and as a result he became embittered.

The consequence was that when he came up with his calculating machine, he was prepared to demonstrate it to members of the Royal Society (including Babbage) but was absolutely not prepared to show anyone the plans in case they pirated it. He had built the machine himself, using wood, so it was larger than if it had been made in metal. He wrote:

> This machine was constructed entirely with my own hands
> (principally in wood) with the utmost regard to economy and
> merely to put my ideas of this mode of calculation into some
> form of action; it is about six feet long, one foot deep and three
> feet wide. In brass & iron it might be constructed so as not to
> occupy a space much larger than a good portable writing desk
> and with powers such as I have described.

So it was rather more economical of space than Babbage's 2.5m high 15 tonne machine, though perhaps the size of calculations Fowler intended were smaller. Its great advance over Babbage was that instead of using the decimal system it used the ternary system, which made it much less complicated. (Electronic machines today use the binary system.) Fowler's son later wrote:

> The government of the day refused even to look at my father's machine on the express ground that they had spent such large sums, with no satisfactory result, on Babbage's 'Calculating Engine', as he termed it.

Thomas Fowler died shortly after constructing his machine, and his secrets were lost. But at least we still have our central heating by which to remember him warmly.

The kitchen range

In 1802 the Exeter ironfounder George Bodley invented the very first kitchen range – a cast-iron stove in which the fire was totally enclosed, with a flue to extract the gases produced by burning. It had both an oven, ideal for slow cooking, and a stove top as well, and was produced in various models, from the 'Cottage' size upwards.

It was immensely popular, both in Britain and abroad, and was perhaps the most successful product of the foundry, one of several in Exeter, which survived for 177 years.

Axminster carpets

For this invention, I can do no better than quote *Murray's Handbook for Travellers in Devon and Cornwall*, 1872 edition:

> [Axminster] is widely known in connection with the carpets which for many years were manufactured in the Court House, close to the church, and were first made here by a Mr Whitty, in 1755, who was rewarded for his ingenuity with the medal of the Society of Arts. These celebrated fabrics were far superior to anything of the kind which had been previously produced in England: rather glaring in colour, but for durability considered equal to the carpets brought from Turkey. Their excellence in this respect was due to their having been made entirely by hand,

like tapestry. The manufacture is now carried on at Wilton, near Salisbury, but the rugs alone are hand-made, the carpets are woven. The factory at Axminster has been closed since 1835.

In fact manufacture in Axminster had ceased in 1828, due to a disastrous fire. Whitty's products were purchased for places like the Prince Regent's Brighton Pavilion, and a massive carpet was even woven for the Sultan of Turkey.

Carpet manufacture restarted in Axminster when a Kidderminster manufacturer decided in 1937 to relocate, a plan disrupted by the outbreak of war, but put into full effect after its conclusion. The modern carpets are of course quite different from Whitty's products: they are woven on power looms, and are particularly valued for their hardwearing qualities by hotels and pubs.

China clay, William Cookworthy and the cure for scurvy

For many readers, this story of Devon's various industrial inventions may come as a complete surprise. Iron foundries in Exeter? The steam engine dreamed up in Dartmouth? These ideas do not fit with the relaxed rural image promoted by modern tourist Devon. But that has not always been Devon's image: when Daniel Defoe published his *Tour through the Whole Island of Great Britain* in 1724, he wrote:

> Devonshire one entire county is so full of great towns, and those towns so full of people, and those people so universally employed in trade, and manufactures, that not only it cannot be equalled in England, but perhaps not in Europe.

And Defoe knew what he was talking about: for the previous 30 years, as well as being a journalist, and writing the odd novel, he had been a trader on his own account and, in addition, worked as an observer – some would say spy – informing the government of the conditions, and the political mood, in various parts of England and Scotland. (He played a significant undercover role prior to the Union of 1707.)

The 'manufactures' he meant were primarily but not exclusively for the cloth trade, still largely a cottage industry, but he makes clear that Plymouth and to a lesser extent Dartmouth were extremely busy maritime hubs. However, there is a suspicion that Defoe had not recently visited Devon when he wrote his *Tour*, which may account for his failure to remark on the ball clay industry which was already supplying material for the Staffordshire potteries as well as local potters.

But the great breakthrough for the extractive industries had yet to come – the discovery of 'china clay', initially in Cornwall around 1760 and later in Devon, by the chemist William Cookworthy (1705-1780), a weaver's son from Kingsbridge.

China clay was essential to the manufacture of porcelain, which had hitherto only been made in China or at Meissen in Germany. Cookworthy opened a factory in Plymouth in 1768 but moved it to Bristol in 1770. Once again the patent laws were problematic: Cookworthy's firm, now run by his cousin, was crippled by 'successfully' defending its rights, this time against Josiah Wedgwood. As a result, a Staffordshire firm bought out the Devon patent.

Cookworthy made two further major contributions which changed the world a bit. When the third Eddystone lighthouse was under construction (see page 16) the engineer Smeaton stayed with Cookworthy, who assisted Smeaton in developing a new kind of hydraulic lime mortar, which was crucial to the construction. Smeaton alone is usually credited with this, but as it was a chemical rather than engineering achievement, surely Cookworthy the chemist played the major part. The result was the development of 'Portland cement', and in due course the use of concrete as a construction material – not least in post-war Plymouth.

Cookworthy also advised naval officers on the prevention of scurvy, by the provision of fresh vegetables, or failing that sauerkraut. Captain Cook and Joseph Banks were guests of Cookworthy prior to embarking on their great (scurvy-free) voyage in 1768.

Pencils and pills

Another serial inventor and polymath was William Brockedon (1787-1854), who inherited his father's Totnes watchmaking business at the age of 14. He was at the same time a talented young artist, and in 1809 went to London to study. He became a regular exhibitor at the Royal Academy over a period of 25 years, and one of his portraits was hung in the Uffizi Gallery in Florence. His 'Christ raising the Widow's Son' is in Dartmouth's parish church.

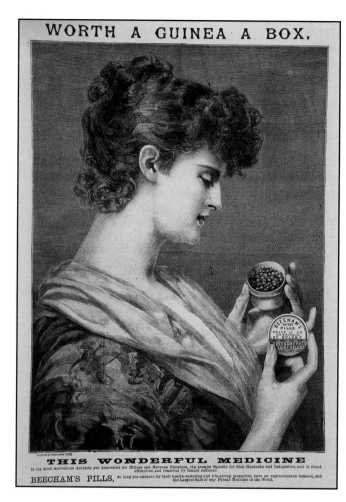

The making of pills was revolutionised by an invention of Devon artist William Brockedon.

(Beecham's Pills were most unusual among Victorian medicines, in that they actually had a beneficial effect.)

At the same time he became a travel writer and illustrator and published *Illustrations of the Passes of the Alps* in 1829 with 40 different routes, following it with other books, including *The Illustrated Road Book from London to Naples*.

As if that were not enough, he invented an improved way of wire drawing, an improved pen nib, and various forms of substitute for corks made from the material of the moment, india rubber. He proposed the idea of gas fires to replace solid fuel, but with the gas visibly ignited in such a way that it looked like a 'real' coal fire.

However his most important contribution was accidental – a new way of making pills which was an adaptation of a machine he had actually designed for making improved pencil leads. Before this time, pills had to be made using moist ingredients to bind the active medicines, which often rendered the drug ineffective.

Brockedon's patent for 'shaping pills, lozenges and black lead by pressure in dies' gave us the convenient form of pill we know today.

Naval test tanks a.k.a. ship-model basins

One Devonian totally changed the way in which ships were, and still are, designed: William Froude (1810-1879). He came from a privileged background, was born at Dartington Parsonage, the son of Archdeacon Froude of Totnes, and was educated at Westminster School and Oxford, where he obtained a first in maths in 1832.

His first job was surveying for the South Eastern Railway, then he joined Brunel's team, where he came up with the 'track transition curve', providing the best transition from a straight section to a curve, whether in a railway track or a road, and he also managed the construction of a section of the Bristol-Exeter line.

Brunel then persuaded him to look at ship design, in particular at ways of designing hulls for greater stability. His theoretical paper presented in 1861 to the Institute of Naval Architects was well received, and had an immediate effect on warship design.

But Froude was not content with theory: he was able to demonstrate using model ships that reality was more complicated than theories predicted, for example some blunt prows cut through water better than some sharp prows. So it wasn't possible to arrive at the very best design for a hull purely by theory, but it *was* possible to try out different model designs, and then use a mathematical formula he had worked out to predict accurately the results once the design was scaled up from model to finished vessel. The formula is called the 'Froude number'.

The Admiralty was so impressed that they built the world's first naval test tank at Froude's house, Chelston Cross in Torquay, so that he could conduct tests there. The tank was 82m x 12m x 3m deep, and a steam engine was provided to pull the models through it. Froude also developed an instrument to measure the performance of propellers.

With relatively minor changes, his methods are apparently still in use today.

The Eddystone lighthouses

So far the changes described have been initiated by Devonians, which is not the case here, but the story of the Eddystone is so remarkable that perhaps it deserves a place, since this lighthouse was the first in the world to be be built on an exposed rock in the open sea.

The Eddystone Rocks are submerged at high tide, and lie about 20 km south-south-west from Plymouth, directly in the path of vessels heading in from the Atlantic. They were an appalling hazard but building a lighthouse seemed an impossibility, until Henry Winstanley (1644-1703) took up the challenge.

Winstanley was born in Saffron Walden, south of Cambridge, and became Clerk of the Works at Audley End House – which Charles II used as his base when he went to Newmarket races. On the outside of his own house Winstanley fitted a lantern and various clocks, but he was an eccentric and inside the house he made joke chairs, which moved when sat on or trapped the sitter with their arms, not to mention a ghost which leapt up from the floor if you kicked an old slipper. He charged an entrance fee for visitors to see these 'Wonders'.

He followed the success of this venture by opening a 'theatre' – though it had more in common with a theme park – in London's Piccadilly. It was called Winstanley's Water Works, and there were numerous extravagant inventions to be seen – flying dragons and pyrotechnics. He even had a 'Wonderful Barrel' which served up hot or cold drinks.

The attraction paid well, and he invested his profits in ships. Two of these were wrecked on the Eddystone Rocks, and Winstanley offered to build a lighthouse there, an offer which the Admiralty happily accepted, as nobody else had been prepared to do it.

Work began in 1696, but progress was slow, because access to the wave-swept reef was so difficult. In the first summer, all they managed was 12 holes drilled in the rocks, on which the structure could be built. But by 1698 it was complete, though Winstanley kept making improvements. Perhaps the ornamental design would have been more appropriate in his Piccadilly theme park, but for five years not a single ship was lost on the Eddystone.

Winstanley was rightly proud, and had great confidence in the

Left: Winstanley's lighthouse
Right: the disastrous fire in Rudyerd's timber lighthouse

structure. He expressed a wish to be in his lighthouse at the time of 'the greatest storm there ever was' – and his wish came true. On the night of 27 November 1703 there occurred 'the Great Storm' which caused unprecedented damage both on land and at sea. The Royal Navy alone lost 13 ships and 1500 men drowned, and perhaps 15,000 lives were lost in total.

Winstanley and his lighthouse simply disappeared without trace. No ship had been lost on the Eddystone for five years, but a few days later the *Winchelsea*, arriving from Virginia and not knowing the lighthouse had gone, drove straight onto the rocks.

But Winstanley had demonstrated that the task was not impossible. The next builder was John Rudyerd (or Rudyard) who was a London silk merchant born in Staffordshire. That sounds a bizarre background for a lighthouse builder, but Rudyerd soon showed he knew what he was doing. He had 36 conical holes drilled in the rock, wider at the bottom than at the top, and filled these with molten pewter, which gave him a base for the structure. The building was made of alternate layers of stone and timber, but the whole was covered with massive vertical timbers, designed like the hull of a ship. It was an extremely elegant structure.

For fifty years the sea failed to destroy it, but then a fire in its kitchen set it alight, and the 94 year old keeper, carrying buckets of sea-water up to the top of the tower, failed to put it out. The tower was destroyed, and the keeper died six days later, having, it seems, swallowed molten lead from the roof: the autopsy recovered from his stomach a piece of lead weighing 200 g.

The third light was the work of the great Yorkshire engineer John Smeaton (1724-1792). His innovations included the use of hydraulic lime (see page 11), an extraordinarily complex pattern of dovetailed granite blocks, and an even more elegant design than Rudyerd's.

This lighthouse stood for 123 years, and never had a problem – until the rock beneath it began to be undermined. A new tower was built on an adjacent rock in 1882. It was decided to deconstruct Smeaton's light and rebuild it at Plymouth, where the upper part of the tower is nowadays the focal point of the Hoe.

The diving machine

Shipwrecks were not a disaster for everyone. One Devonian who made a fortune from them was John Lethbridge, an unsuccessful wool merchant from Newton Abbot, who invented a 'machine' that could be used to salvage treasure from wrecks. This is how he described it:

> Necessity is the mother of invention, and being in the year 1715 quite reduced, and having a large family, my thoughts turned upon some extraordinary method to retrieve my misfortunes and was prepossessed that it might be practicable to contrive a machine to recover from wrecks lost in the sea; and the first step I took towards it was going into a hogshead, upon land, bunged up tight, where I stayed half-an-hour without communication of air; then I made a trench, near a well, at the bottom of my orchard in this place in order to convey a sufficient quantity of

16

water to cover the hogshead, and then tried how long I could live under water without air-pipes of communication of air and found I could stay longer under water than upon land.

This experiment being tried, I then began to think of making my engine, which was soon made by a cooper in Stanhope Street, London, of which you have the following description.

It is made of wainscot, perfectly round, about six feet in length, about two foot and a half diameter at the head and about eighteen inches diameter at the foot, and contains about thirty gallons; it is hooped with iron hoops without and within to guard against pressure. There are two holes for the arms and a glass about four inches diameter, and an inch and a quarter thick, to look through, which is fixed in the bottom part, so as to be in a direct line with the eyes, two air-holes upon the upper part, into one of which air is conveyed by a pair of bellows, both of which are stopped with plugs immediately before going down to the bottom. At the foot part, there's a hole to let out water. Sometime, there's a large rope fixed to the back or upper part, by which it is let down, and there's a little line called the signal line, by which the people above are directed what to do, and under which is fixed a piece of timber as a guard for the glass.

I go in with my feet foremost and when my arms are got through the holes, then the head is put on, which is fastened with screws, It requires 5 cwt to sink it, and take 15 pound weight from it, and it will buoy upon the surface of the water. I lie straight upon my breast all the time I am in the engine, which hath many times been more than six hours, being frequently refreshed upon the surface by a pair of bellows.

Whilst Lethbridge's machine could not go deeper than about 15 metres without leaking due to the increased presssure, there were many wrecks in relatively shallow water, and he was not confined to British waters, but was hired by the East India Company and others to dive on wrecks at the Cape of Good Hope, Madeira and the West Indies. As a result he became a wealthy man, and bought an estate in Kingskerswell.

The arts and scholarship

Devon has been responsible for fewer innovations in the arts than in science and engineering, and cannot really be said to have 'changed the world'. For example the great portrait miniaturist Nicholas Hilliard, and Sir Joshua Reynolds, the leading English painter of his age, were major painters but both quite conservative in their technique.

Devon was the birthplace of Samuel Taylor Coleridge, one of the founders of English Romanticism. He was a very original poet in his own right, who also greatly influenced Wordsworth towards the use of 'ordinary' rather than 'poetic' language – but he was sent away from Devon at the age of nine, and the verse he wrote when visiting Devon as a Cambridge student shows little sign of that originality: it was the subsequent stimulus of meeting Southey, and later the Wordsworths, that brought it out.

The Bodleian Library

The founding of Oxford University's library by Sir Thomas Bodley (1545-1613) might be thought to come in the same category, in that it was a refounding of an existing institution, and of course there were many earlier libraries. Magnificent as this one became, both under Bodley's management and subsequently, the concept was not original – but two features *were* original. The first was the installation at the entrance to the library of an extremely impressive 'Register of Donations', a book in which recent benefactors' names were very publicly honoured, which strangely had a most productive effect on the rate of financial donations.

The second was an arrangement Bodley reached with the Stationers' Company that their members would present a gratis copy of every new publication to the Bodleian Library. The successor to this arrangement is enshrined in the copyright acts, and every British publisher is obliged to present a copy of every new title to the British Library, the National Libraries of Scotland and Wales, and the university libraries in Oxford, Cambridge and Dublin.

Thomas Bodley was born in Exeter. When Queen Mary came to the throne in 1553, his father, a Protestant merchant, chose to go abroad rather than live under a Roman Catholic regime which he correctly thought would prove intolerant, taking his family (and incidentally Nicholas Hilliard, two years younger than Thomas Bodley) with him. Thomas Bodley in consequence was able to study in Geneva under Calvin and learn Greek and Hebrew, as well of course as assimilating European languages.

When the family returned after Mary's death, the young Bodley was given a position at court, and became an MP. He was soon made ambassador in the Hague. Around 1598 he resigned as a diplomat and devoted the rest of his life to book collection.

Scientific archaeology

Another extraordinary contribution to our understanding of the world came from William Pengelly of Torquay (1812-1894), who was actually born in Cornwall, the son of the master of a small coasting vessel. He received no formal schooling after the age of twelve, but by self-education, especially in mathematics, became accepted among the leading scientists of his day. It was not easy:

> My only chance of obtaining a book was through an old pedlar, who occasionally visited our village [Looe], and of whom I bought my first 'Euclid.' Well do I remember the delight with which, on one occasion, I purchased twenty volumes of books at a secondhand bookshop at Devonport – ay, and the pride, too, with which I carried my treasure in a bundle on my shoulder, to my village home, sixteen miles across the Cornish hills. I could tell, too, of the derision of some of my acquaintances, the dissuasive advice of others, and the firm, though kind and well-meant, opposition of my parents. In short, I stood all but alone; few, very few, sympathized or cheered, but many scoffed.

Around 1836 he moved to Torquay and opened a school; ten years later he gave up the school and became a private tutor, which allowed him more freedom for other pursuits. His private pupils were both numerous and extremely wealthy, and included two Russian princes and a Dutch princess – useful, because this teaching was his only source of income and supported his other activities.

He also founded the Torquay Mechanics' Institute (where he gave lectures without pay), the Torquay Natural History Society and what is now known as the Devonshire Association. Through a visit to King's College London, he became acquainted with some of the leading scientists of the day.

One of his great interests was Devonshire geology, in which he was soon the leading expert. There had already been excavations at Kent's Cavern, where there was clear evidence of ancient human occupation, but no way of proving its age. Scientists and naturalists – let alone religious zealots – were at that time very much at odds over the age of the earth, and of the human race. There were those, including Philip Gosse in St Marychurch, who believed literally in the Bible, which purportedly said that the world had been created in 4004 BC, and they would not accept geological evidence to the contrary.

When a previously unknown cave was discovered in Brixham, with its deposits absolutely undisturbed, Pengelly saw it as a wonderful opportunity, and obtained funding for its exploration, on entirely new principles. Rather than digging test pits looking for finds, he would re-move all the deposits layer by layer, meticulously recording the precise position of every piece of evidence. This is called stratigraphy, and is of course familiar now to anyone who has ever seen an archaeology programme on TV, but at that time it was revolutionary. The results were dramatic. Pengelly wrote:

> The sceptical position of the authorities in geological science remained unaffected, however, until 1859 when the discovery and systematic exploration of a comparatively small virgin cavern on Windmill Hill at Brixham led to a sudden and complete revolution; for it was seen that whatever were the facts elsewhere, there had undoubtedly been found at Brixham flint implements commingled with the remains of the mammoth and his companions, and in such a way as to render it impossible to doubt that man occupied Devonshire before the extinction of the cave mammals.

It was the technique of stratigraphy that mattered. The excavations at Brixham were followed by further excavations at Kent's Cavern and elsewhere, which provided more evidence. The methods invented by Pengelly had revolutionised cave exploration and laid the foundations for an entirely new scientific approach to archaeology, which would in time be able to date the development of humankind.

Local history and landscape

WG Hoskins (1908-1992) was born in Exeter where his father and grandfather (both also William George) and his great grandfather, had been bakers. He attended what would later become Exeter University, reading economics and subsequently specialising in the economic history of Devon. He became a lecturer at University College Leicester, where his own researches were very wide-ranging.

In 1948 he became Reader in English Local History at Leicester; this was the first ever university department in the subject. At that time, academic historians often failed to take local history seriously, dismissing it as something for retired dabblers or underemployed clergymen who were little better than antiquarians. Hoskins successfully challenged this view, along with other historians such as Arthur Raistrick, the Yorkshire geologist and pioneer of industrial history. Hoskins called for 'patient and minute topographical research – of a sort that is wrongly despised by most historians'.

But his most famous work, *The Making of the English Landscape* (1955) was aimed not at the academic world but at the general reader, 'the man who wishes to forget income tax, hydrogen bombs and the relentless march of science' and instead go country walking. It was the first attempt at a coherent explanation of the landscape which we see around us as being almost entirely man-made. Over the next few decades, this book made many people (including myself) see their world with new eyes.

Its tone is often far from academic history – the very first word of the very first chapter is 'Wordsworth…' – and it contains rapturous imaginings of the landscape seen by the first human beings to arrive in England, as well as a horror of early nineteenth century industrialists and of the ugliness of the 1950s post-war scene – prefabs, military airfields and arterial roads. To be fair, we should remember that Britain was visually a much less attractive place back then, when we still had an active manufacturing industry, coal mines, and industrial towns black with soot and thick with smog, but many people even then criticised the book as too Romantic, harking back to ancient days when England had apparently resembled the Garden of Eden.

It is hardly surprising that Hoskins later had great success with a series of TV programmes.

More than sixty-five years have passed since the book's publication, during which time generations of historians and archaeologists have been inspired by Hoskins and followed up the leads he suggested, with the inevitable result that much of the argument of his great book is now seen as dated or over-simplistic.

Whilst *The Making of the English Landscape* was Hoskins' most significant work, and in a small way changed the world, his book *Devon* with its gazetteer of every single parish in the county (all of them apparently visited by public transport or on foot, as Hoskins did not drive) is seen by many as a much quieter but even greater achievement. This book is still of use.

The Elizabethan sea dogs

At no point have I suggested that every change brought about by a Devonian made the world a better place, and in this section there are some changes whose merits will depend on your point of view, and others which leave no doubt whatsoever. For example, Sir John Hawkins took England into the slave trade – though he certainly didn't invent it.

Drake, Raleigh, Hawkins, Gilbert, Davis and others are (or were) household names, either as explorers, entrepreneurs of early (failed) attempts to colonise North America, or as fighters against the wicked Spanish. Many of them are certainly larger than life characters, often parading massively inflated egos and quite extraordinary selfishness.

They indulged in piracy and in the case of the half-brothers Humphrey Gilbert and Walter Raleigh were guilty of what we would now regard as gruesome genocidal war crimes in Ireland.

Leadership does of course require self-confidence, and perhaps for several of these men their success in part stemmed from a ruthless conviction of the rightness of their own actions. It is probably the case that the greatest change they wrought in the world was not as individuals in their own time, but in being adopted as state heroes in the Victorian period – with any war crimes conveniently forgotten. Their 'can-do' attitude was emphasised in order to make them exemplars for children who might later find themselves sent out to rule a little patch of the Empire – though Hawkins was an embarrassment even to the imperial enthusiasts.

They remained in vogue as long as the world in school atlases was predominantly pink. But don't misunderstand me: not all of them were villains!

Stephen Borough (1525-1584)

Stephen and his younger brother William were brought up at Northam Burrows. Stephen participated with his uncle in coastal surveys of Devon and Cornwall, which led to improved fortifications at Plymouth, Dartmouth, Teignmouth and Exmouth. During this time he learned his navigational skills from a Spanish textbook and in the process also learned Spanish, which was to be very important to him. It should be remembered that for much of the Tudor period Spain was not an enemy, and sometimes was regarded as an ally. Queen Mary was married to the Spanish king.

From 1553 Borough was involved in expeditions to explore a northeast passage to China, which he did not succeed in traversing, but he certainly reached the port of Archangel in 1553. He was then invited to the court of Tsar Ivan (as yet not considered Terrible) in Moscow for the winter. On the next voyage he reached Vaygach Island, even further east. Rather than keep his knowledge to himself, Borough shared it with the whole of the Muscovy Company.

During Queen Mary's reign, he travelled to Seville and was permitted to see how Spanish pilots were trained, perhaps in return for sharing his Arctic knowledge. He brought back a Spanish training manual, which was translated and published in 1561 as *The Arte of Navigation* and remained a key text for decades to come.

He continued to make voyages to Arctic Russia until, in 1563, he began to work for the Navy, living at Chatham, where he made improvements both in the dockyard and in the design and construction of ships. From 1572 he was Master of Trinity House, and had a great influence on pilot training. His brother was also an important naval administrator.

Sir John Hawkins (1532-1595)

Hawkins was the son of a ship-owning merchant of Plymouth, and was a 'common councillor' in Plymouth by the age of 26. He conceived the idea of making the existing 'triangle trade' (from Europe to the African coast, to the West Indies and back to England) more profitable by collecting slaves, for which he obtained backing from a London syndicate.

On his first voyage he seized by force slaves who were already on board a Portuguese slave-trading ship, which was cheaper than buying them, and sold them in the Caribbean to the new Spanish colonies. His second voyage was backed by Queen Elizabeth, and he was accompanied by his cousin Francis Drake. Despite two of his ships being seized by the Spanish authorities, who wanted to prevent the English trading at all in their territories, this voyage too was a financial success.

The third voyage was more problematic, as relations with Spain were getting tricky. Hawkins had to fight within Africa to obtain his slave cargo, then an unprovoked attack by the Spanish led to a six hour naval battle at San Juan d'Uloa in which all but two of his ships were lost. Of 320 crew, only 15 got back home, as well as Hawkins and Drake, and 30 were left as Spanish prisoners. Nonetheless, *financially* it was a success, and these three voyages led other merchants to emulate them. The English slave trade had begun.

The next episode in Hawkins' life is mysterious. He became a government spy and successfully pretended to the Spanish ambassador that he was part of the Ridolfi plot, the aim of which was to support the 'Rising of the North' by landing a Spanish army in England, assassinating Queen Elizabeth and putting Mary Queen of Scots on the throne. Hawkins was able to pass the names of the conspirators to the Secretary of State, William Cecil. This and other information allowed Cecil to foil the plot.

Hawkins was rewarded by being made MP for Plymouth, where he and his brother set about making it the centre of England's naval defences. In 1578 he became Treasurer of the Navy, where he initiated major changes. He wanted fewer but better paid, and therefore more committed, sailors, and he improved ship design. The hulls were better sheathed, detachable topmasts were introduced, and the ships were

A Victorian illustration of the Battle of San Juan d'Uloa

made longer, with lower forecastles and poops. When the Armada arrived, these new English ships were much more manoeuvrable than the old-fashioned Spanish galleons, which gave them a huge advantage. For this we have to thank Hawkins. He was third in command during the battle, and was knighted during the engagement.

After the Armada victory, Hawkins and Drake set about the activity both really enjoyed – state-sponsored piracy. They were instructed to make a voyage to capture Panama, but given joint command – a disastrous idea because whilst Hawkins was a careful planner by nature, Drake always acted totally on impulse – and did not take kindly to his views being questioned. The situation was made even worse because Queen Elizabeth vacillated in her instructions, and when finally they did sail, Drake hadn't loaded enough victuals. Both Hawkins and Drake died at sea during the voyage.

There is one further way in which Hawkins changed the world a bit, and not for the better. In July 1565 he was the first European to spot a local custom:

> The Floridians… have a kinde of herbe dryed who, with a cane, and an earthen cup in the end, with fire, and the dried herbs put together do sucke thoro' the cane the smoke thereof…

It was Hawkins, not Raleigh, who brought tobacco and smoking to England, though it was Raleigh who made it popular at Court, after which the fashion spread elsewhere.

The first English colony

There had of course been Spanish and Portuguese colonies in the Americas, but the first attempt to found an English colony in North America was made by Devonian Sir Humphrey Gilbert, who in 1578 obtained a six year licence to seize land in Newfoundland for the Crown. Gilbert seems to have been a man both murderous and incompetent, whose motto was *Quid non?*, Why not? As in, this man stands in my way: why not kill him? That was certainly his attitude in Ireland.

Despite his royal licence, he failed to organise any colonists but did finally get to Newfoundland, clashed with the fishermen of various countries who spent the summer months living on the shores of Newfoundland, levied taxes on them, dug a piece of turf to claim ownership (following the feudal custom called livery of seisin), then set off back to England without making any attempt at settlement.

Rejecting the views of the experienced sailors around him, Gilbert chose his own course, ran his largest ship aground and wrecked it, then insisted on staying on the *Squirrel*, the smaller of the two remaining ships, which was clearly unfit to face the stormy weather they would meet. He could be seen sitting at the stern, apparently reading More's *Utopia*, and was heard to call out several times, 'We are as near to Heaven by sea as by land!'

That night the *Squirrel* was overwhelmed by the storm, and sank with all hands including Gilbert.

Sir Humphrey's half-brother Walter Raleigh was a favourite of the Queen, so was granted a repeat of Gilbert's licence. It was made clear to Raleigh that what England needed in the short run was a base from which privateers could intercept Spanish treasure ships. He sent first an exploratory expedition in 1584, then in 1585 a fleet of seven vessels led by Sir Richard Grenville, a cousin of Raleigh's described by a contemporary as having 'intolerable pride and insatiable ambition'.

A base was established at Roanoke Island, a gratuitous attack was made to destroy a native village which inevitably aroused local hostility, then Grenville left for England, capturing a Spanish vessel on the way to help pay for the trip.

When he returned the following year, he found the colony deserted: Francis Drake (whom he already had reason to hate) had picked up the colonists, who were short of food and under pressure from the resentful locals. Grenville left a small group of sailors to protect Raleigh's 'right' to the 'colony', doubtless gnashed his teeth, and set off for a spot of recuperative pillaging in the Azores.

Raleigh's response was to send a further batch of 115 colonists, with John White, a gentleman artist who had been on the previous expedition and produced splendidly sympathetic paintings of the native people, as Governor. They were supposed to go to Chesapeake, but first to call and rescue the earlier colonists. On arrival at Roanoke in 1587 they found nothing but one skeleton.

At this point their Portuguese navigator Simon Fernandez in effect mutinied, and insisted the new colonists remain at Roanoke because summer was over, and there was no time to go to Chesapeake. The colonists persuaded White to return to England to explain their plight. He bravely crossed the Atlantic in late Autumn, leaving behind his daughter and baby grand-daughter, the first English person born in North America, and all his possessions.

When he arrived in England, he found there was an order that no ships were allowed to leave, all being required to repel the expected invasion by the Armada. He hired two boats too small for military service, but inevitably they were equally unsuitable for an Atlantic crossing. It was three years before he managed to return to Roanoke.

When he finally did so, in effect as a passenger on a privateering venture funded by Raleigh, the settlement was deserted, but with the word 'Croatan' prominently carved on a tree – Croatan being a nearby island, to which the colonists had presumably moved. A storm was brewing and the privateer's sailors were not prepared to stay. White was given no choice. The colonists were abandoned. There are many theories as to what happened to them, but no certainty.

It is hard to escape the conclusion that this attempt at colonisation failed firstly because it was conceived as a commercial privateering venture to make a few Devon gentlemen (and the Queen) rich, rather than for the good of the colonists themselves, and then because it was led by Sir Richard Grenville, lord of the manor of Bideford.

Shortly after this, Grenville would throw away his life and those of many of his crew, as well as one of England's best ships, in a ridiculous and unnecessary fight, when he disobeyed his Admiral's orders and deliberately took the *Revenge* into the middle of a Spanish fleet.

Tennyson in a famous poem made him out to be a hero, but a more realistic assessment might be dangerous and suicidal idiot.

Some lesser strides for mankind

The first Christmas card

The first Christmas card, or to be more precise the first commercially produced Christmas card, was designed at Orestone Manor, Maidencombe, Torquay, in 1840 and was sold for Christmas 1843.

Prior to that people had exchanged letters at Christmas, and sometimes hand-made cards. This was perhaps more common in America than in Britain, because in 1822 the Superintendent of Mails in Washington DC was complaining that he needed to hire sixteen additional postmen, saying 'I don't know what we'll do if it keeps on.'

In 1840 Henry Cole, later Sir Henry, was reorganising the Public Record Office in London, having previously assisted Rowland Hill in starting the penny post. Rather than writing numerous seasonal letters himself, he had an artist design a card for him. It showed a family enjoying themselves with festive drinks, and, to either side, scenes of charitable giving to the poor.

It already said 'A Merry Christmas and a Happy New Year', so the sender just needed to fill in the 'To…' and 'From…' lines.

This was well received and Cole decided to have it commercially printed in 1843. About 2000 were printed, but how many of them

The first commercial Christmas card

were sold is not known. They were priced at 1 shilling each (5p) at a time when farm labourers were paid 9 shillings a week, and even office workers were glad to take home 25 shillings a week.

The artist was John Callcott Horsley, who apparently built Orestone Manor, now a hotel. Torquay was doubtless a good place to get portrait commissions, though he spent much of his time in London. Horsley's sister married Isambard Kingdom Brunel, who loved the area and began building his own country estate nearby.

Horsley subsequently became Rector of the Royal Academy, where he became notorious for his opposition to the use of nude models, writing a letter to *The Times* signed 'British Matron'. *Punch* magazine referred to him as Mr J C(lothes) Horsley.

The Jack Russell

Parson Jack Russell (1795-1883) was a famous Victorian example of a type more common in the eighteenth century, the clergyman who had very little interest in performing clerical duties, but a great deal of interest in country sports, in his case specifically hunting. To be fair, as vicar of Swimbridge in north Devon he did live in his parish, which is more than can be said for many of his contemporaries, and he was liked by his parishioners. You can find stories about him in James Whinray's *Tales from Devon Folklore* (Bossiney Books).

He was born at Dartmouth and educated at Blundell's School Tiverton. While at Oxford he bought a white terrier called Trump from a local milkman. He then bred from her a line of fox-hunting terriers which came to be known as Jack Russells. The aim was that they should have stamina to run with the hunt and also courage to chase the fox underground.

As a founding member of the Kennel Club, Russell refused to show his own animals, on the grounds that they were so far superior to all others that there was no point. (Since he'd written the breed standard based on his own dogs' attributes, he may have been correct!)

The 'father of baseball'

Henry Chadwick (1824-1908), half-brother of the great sanitary reformer Sir Edwin Chadwick, was born in Exeter. His family moved to Brooklyn in 1835. He played cricket and rounders (a game which dates from Tudor times) and became a cricket journalist. He first saw baseball in 1856, and soon began to write reports of baseball matches. He was prominent in the popularisation of the game, influenced the development of the rules, and was an obsessive compiler of statistics. He devised new ways of reporting scores, especially the 'box score'.

The first Ladies Golf Club?

The Royal North Devon Golf Club on Northam Burrows is the oldest course in England, dating from 1864. A Westward Ho! Ladies Golf Club, with a separate course, was started in 1868. The ladies were accompanied by gentleman caddies dressed in scarlet uniforms. There had been a Ladies Putting Club at St Andrews from 1867, and since the Westward Ho! players were allowed only one club, and that a putter, probably St Andrews should take precedence.

Devon changing the future? More Utopias?

You might expect to find the Pilgrim Fathers here, since they were most certainly idealists and much is made of their departure from Plymouth, but in reality they had little if anything to do with Devon. The nucleus of the group was a separatist religious congregation from

Nottinghamshire. From there they had emigrated to Leiden in the Netherlands, being convinced that their religious beliefs were incompatible with the Church of England. But they did not wish to become Dutch, so they had then decided to settle in America.

The *Speedwell* and the *Mayflower* had departed from Leiden, but leaks forced them to make unplanned stops first at Dartmouth, and then at Plymouth for repairs, and to sell the unseaworthy *Speedwell*.

Dartington Hall

Dartington Hall was purchased by Leonard and Dorothy Elmhirst in 1925, the year of their marriage. Dorothy, née Whitney, who was extremely wealthy and from a prominent American family, had already begun to devote her wealth to philanthropic work. Her first husband died in the 'flu pandemic following WW1, and she married Leonard Elmhirst, a Yorkshireman whose experience helping in rural India had led him to study agriculture at Cornell University in New York state. He was much influenced by Rabindranath Tagore.

It was probably Tagore who suggested that the Elmhirsts buy Dartington Hall, where they hoped simultaneously to revive the local rural economy and promote the arts. They, and later the Trust which they set up to manage the project, founded a private school with 'progressive values', as well as the Dartington College of Arts, an International Summer School of music, and many other projects including the Beaford Arts centre in North Devon.

The rural regeneration aspect has among other things included a shopping complex, now 'Shops at Dartington', formerly known as the Cider Press Centre, and the glass-making company Dartington Crystal, though the Trust sold its interest in that firm some years ago. At Dartington Hall itself the Trust runs a hotel.

Transition towns and the Totnes Pound

The 'transition town' movement was founded by Rob Hopkins, who is from Totnes, though he came up with the idea when teaching at a college at Kinsale, County Cork. It has been enthusiastically received and has rapidly spread around the world, with over a thousand 'transition initiatives' registered. 'Transition' refers to the need for us to face up to the changes society will have to make as a result of climate change, and of ending our dependency on oil.

Communities will clearly need to become locally resilient, and the movement stresses local involvement in thinking these ideas through, rather than expecting experts coming in with clip-boards to tell us how to do it. It also promotes the idea that the future should be seen as an opportunity, rather than as a threat.

The areas which participants need to consider include reducing the energy used as a result of long supply chains, in particular to source as much food as possible locally; and to reduce waste, especially commercial waste, by finding ways of recycling.

Totnes was the first place to develop a transition model on these lines. It was the first place to start its own currency – the Totnes Pound – in 2007. The Totnes pound was of identical value to the pound sterling, but if someone accepted payment in this currency, it could of course only be spent in Totnes, where many of the traders would accept it. The idea was to cause people, Totnesians especially, to buy locally – and to buy from the smaller shops, rather than from branches of national chains, which were unlikely to accept the local currency. The Totnes pound continued in use until 2019.

It is easy to be sceptical about idealism. Aside from the questions of financial responsibility and regulation which a local currency raises, has the transition town movement, in its opposition to globalisation, become *too* parochial? Idealists have different and sometimes contradictory ideals: identifying, let alone achieving Utopia will never be easy.

Out of this world

Finally, a mind-blowing achievement by Devonian bacteria, changing our view of the world. In 2008 a chunk of rock from the cliff face at Beer was sent to the International Space station, and spent 553 days on its outside surface. The rock contained a colony of bacteria, and the experiment was to test whether they would survive without oxygen, exposed to extreme temperature changes, cosmic rays and ultra-violet light. And survive they did, giving support to the idea that life could have arrived on earth carried by a meteorite.